Award-winning writer, Leslie Kenton is the author
of numerous best sellers and has been described in the
press as 'the guru of health and fitness and the most
original voice in health'. A shining example of energy and
commitment, she is highly respected for her thorough
reporting. Leslie was born in California, and is the daughter
of jazz musician Stan Kenton. After leaving Stanford
University she journeyed to Europe in her early twenties,
settling first in Paris, then in Britain, where she has since
remained. She has raised four children on her own by
working as a television broadcaster, novelist, writer and
teacher on health and for fourteen years she was an editor
at *Harpers & Queen*.

Leslie's writing on mainstream health is internationally
known and has appeared in *Vogue*, *The Sunday Times*,
Cosmopolitan and the *Daily Mail*. She is author of many
other health books including: *The New Raw Energy*, *Raw
Energy Recipes* and *Endless Energy* – co-authored with her
daughter Susannah – *The New Biogenic Diet*, *The New Joy of
Beauty*, *The New Ageless Ageing*, *Cellulite Revolution*, *10 Day
Clean-Up Plan*, *Nature's Child*, *Lean Revolution*, *10 Day
De-Stress Plan*, *Passage to Power* and most recently, *Raw
Energy Food Combining Diet* and *Juice High*. She turned to
fiction with *Ludwig* – her first novel. Former consultant to a
medical corporation in the USA and to the Open
University's Centre of Continuing Education, Leslie's
writing has won several awards including the PPA
'Technical Writer of the Year'. Her work was honoured by
her being asked to deliver the McCarrison Lecture at the
Royal Society of Medicine. In recent years she has become
increasingly concerned not only with the process of
enhancing individual health but also with re-establishing
bonds with the earth as part of helping to heal the planet.

Also available in the QUICK FIX series
Lose Fat
Get Fit
Boost Energy
Sleep Deep
Beat Stress

Look Great

LESLIE KENTON

VERMILION
LONDON

13 5 7 9 10 8 6 4 2

First published in the United Kingdom in 1996
by Vermilion
an imprint of Ebury Press
Random House
20 Vauxhall Bridge Road
London SW1V 2SA

Random House Australia (Pty) Limited
20 Alfred Street, Milsons Point, Sydney,
New South Wales 2061, Australia

Random House New Zealand Limited
18 Poland Road, Glenfield,
Auckland 10, New Zealand

Random House South Africa (Pty) Limited
PO BOX 337, Bergvlei, South Africa

Random House Canada
1265 Aerowood Drive, Mississauga
Ontario L4W 1B9, Canada

Random House UK Limited Reg. No, 954009

A CIP catalogue record for this book is available from the
British Library

ISBN: 0 09 181470 7

Printed and bound in Great Britain by
Cox & Wyman Ltd., Reading, Berkshire

Contents

Introduction

Take one handful of self-awareness, a generous portion of style, a spoonful of individuality and a pinch of wit. It's the archetypal recipe for glamour. And today's glamour is a whole new story. That glamour is always changing is what gives it its power. Glamour now demands that you be yourself and express it. There is a new kind of boldness afoot. You see it in the surprising, fresh new colours used for make-up, in freer hairstyles and in a way of dressing that encourages you to mix unpredictable combinations.

In some ways glamour is easier to achieve today because there is such emphasis on individuality. But in lots of ways new glamour is tougher too. Now there is no way you can hide neglect. That is why today's glamour begins from the *inside*, with a body that is strong and firm and vibrantly healthy, with eyes that shine and skin that glows, giving off a sustained radiance which comes from abundant energy. Today's glamour is hard work. It means eliminating from your life whatever is detrimental to you, such as junk food and excessive stress. It also means committing yourself to regularly practised relaxation or meditation, exercise and the very best diet you can manage. Only after this is it time for 'show time', the externals from first-rate skin and hair care to creative make-up and nails.

How you look matters. Not in some superficial or narcissistic way. It matters because the way you look is a reflection of how you feel about yourself and your life and how well you care for yourself. When you look good, you bring pleasure to those who know you – your partner, your children, friends and workmates.

chapter 1

The Skin Challenge

Lasting skin beauty is a question of lasting care, not just spending lavishly on fancy creams and treatments. It is the everyday way you treat skin that matters year after year. But to know how to look after your skin you must first know something about it – how it works, what can be done to care for it well and to prevent it from premature ageing. For only then can you see that its needs are met from day to day. In return it will give you what you desire: beauty that at the very least is skin deep.

Skin Works

A *living, breathing* thing, skin is far more than just a superficial covering for your body. It protects your body from invasion by bacteria, virus, or fungus. It helps eliminate the waste products of the meta-bolism directly through its surface. It helps guard the inside of your body from the destructive ultraviolet rays of the sun. And it registers pleasure and pain from your environment.

Skin is made up of three layers: the outer skin – the *epidermis* (the part you see when you look into the mirror); the living skin – the underlying *dermis*, made up of connective tissue, nerves, blood, and lymph system; and finally the subskin – a fatty layer of *subcutaneous* tissue. To preserve beauty and be truly effective, skin care has to ensure the continuous health and proper functioning of all three layers.

Let's Begin on the Inside

It should go without saying that first-rate nutrition is a must. All the nutrients your body needs for optimum health, your skin needs to keep it young and beautiful, including the vitamins, minerals, proteins, essential fatty acids, trace elements, and unrefined carbohydrates.

Next time you are in the supermarket, take a look at the skin of the woman in front of you and note what she has in her shopping basket. Almost invariably, you'll find that people with beautiful skins are buying lots of fresh fruits and vegetables, while the others have their carts chock-full of refined goods: white flour, sugar, and other industrially prepared goodies.

Proper elimination is also essential for skin health and beauty. You need a diet high in natural fibre, or roughage, from raw vegetables and/or whole grains. Finally, don't forget to drink plenty of water, an essential nutrient you may never have thought of. It helps detoxify skin, dissolving hard debris that interferes with proper circulation and removal of wastes and which can cause cellulite. You should drink at least six to eight big glasses a day for the sake of your skin.

Vitamins for beauty

Some vitamins are particularly vital to the look and

health of the skin. Vitamin A, for instance. If you do not have enough of it in your diet this can bring about dry, scaly, and crinkled skin. Without adequate vitamin C, the collagen fibres in the dermis suffer damage. A lack of one or more of the B complex vitamins can result in redness, tenderness or ulcerations around the corners of the mouth. Vitamin E is vital to skin health and beauty too. Dry, rough, etched, or tired-looking skin often improves when vitamin E is taken in supplementary form. Like vitamin C, vitamin E plays an important role in holding back the skin's ageing process, because of its anti-oxidant properties.

Some of the fatty acids such as GLA from borage oil or evening primrose oil, and the fish oils EPA and DHA taken as supplements have shown themselves to be very helpful in countering a tendency to dry and ageing skin too.

Skin Care from the Outside

There are three parts to any good external skin care regimen, regardless of your age or the type of skin you have:

- Regular, thorough cleansing
- Protection from moisture loss and external roughness
- Protection from the ultraviolet rays of the sun

These three things – cleansing, protection from moisture loss, and a sunscreen, are all there is to basic skin care. They are simple and inexpensive to carry out, and the benefits they bring when used regularly everyday cannot be measured in any amount of money.

Deep cleanse
There are two camps when it comes to cleansing: the soap-and-water lovers and the soap-and-water haters. Both – within reason – are right.

Soap is an excellent cleanser. It removes grease and dirt from the skin's surface easily (although it is usually not as effective at removing make-up as cream or lotion cleansers). Soap is capable of penetrating the skin's outer protective layers, making the skin of women who tend towards dry-ness even drier. Surprisingly, it can also have just the opposite effect on skin that tends to be oily. On the other hand, soap does give a sense of cleanliness that most women feel they don't get with cream and lotion cleansers.

Thanks to modern technology, there are now many pH-balanced soaps, foaming cleansers, and detergent bars that don't disturb the pH of the skin, so that if you are a soap fancier you can find one to suit you without many of the disadvantages of the conventional type.

The cream or oil way
The many cream and lotion cleansers, oils, and cleansing milks available now are also good. Put a lotion or cream cleanser on with your hands as you would soap and then tissue it off, repeating the application until the tissue shows no sign of dirt on it. Then follow with tonic or freshener, preferably one without alcohol in it, or simply rinse your face in cool water.

The double treatment

Because cleanliness is so important to lasting skin health and beauty, if you live in a city or a highly industrialized area where air pollution is a particular problem, the oil-and-water technique is the most effective means of all. Many of the cosmetic industry's most expensive ranges are based on this method of cleansing. But you can put together your own system which is just as effective.

Choose a pure vegetable oil, such as cold-pressed sunflower oil, corn oil, or one of the more expensive hazelnut or apricot oils. It is best to buy it in small quantities and keep it in a cool place, preferably in the refrigerator. Pour about a tablespoonful of the oil into the palm of your hand and spread it all over your face, rubbing it in well. (This is a good opportunity to give yourself a gentle massage to stimulate circulation while the oil is leaching up the make-up and grime on your skin.) Then, using pads of damp absorbent cotton-wool wiped over your face, remove the oil and with it much of the dirt on the skin.

You are ready now for the second stage. Wash your skin in warm water and use a pH-balanced soap, detergent bar, or liquid detergent cleanser, adding plenty of water and rubbing gently with the tips of your fingers and the palms of your hands until the whole face is well covered. Now rinse thoroughly ten times in warm water and then splash with cool.

Whichever cleansing method you choose, follow it twice daily. This is the first step in the craft of skin care.

Water Margin

There are literally hundreds of moisturizers on the market. Some are beautifully cool to the touch and scented, others somewhat greasy. For very dry skin by far the most effective way of moisturizing is simply to *prevent* water in the skin from escaping into the air. This you can do by wearing one of the water-in-oil-type emulsions on your face every day, winter and summer.

Water-in-oil emulsions contain a great deal more fat than water, which means they are able to cover the skin with an impermeable film so that excessive water loss doesn't occur. And they are good for both dry and oily skin. For, unlike so many products specifically designed for oily skin, they don't spur the sebaceous glands to produce even more oil in the kind of vicious circle women with oily skin know so well.

Find a moisturizer that you like and wear it every day, applying it twice a day if you can under make-up when you are wearing it or just on its own when you don't. This is the second part of the craft of skin care.

Light Dangers

The third part of everyday skin care is simple: your skin needs to be protected from the sun. This does not just mean when you are lying on the beach, either; it means *all* the time. For ultraviolet light is the worst destroyer and ager of the skin that you are ever likely to encounter. Heavy exposure to the sun's light at the age of eighteen will result in early wrinkling, between twenty-five and forty.

Which sunscreen product you choose depends

on how much light you are exposed to. Many make-up products now include a sunscreen in their formulation (read labels). There are now a few water-resistant sun lotions which make excellent moisturizers-cum-sunscreens for everyday wear too, since they happen to be water-in-oil emulsions. The sunscreen must offer not only a UVB screen against burning but also UVA protection against ageing. It should offer at least an SPF of 4 or more for day to day care in winter or when overcast, rising to a 15 or higher when you will be in direct sunlight. Twenty years from now, when you compare your face with a friend's of the same age who hasn't used a sunscreen constantly, you will be pleased to find that you look a good ten years younger than she does.

Troubleshooting

Theoretically, having beautiful skin is simple. Take one part clear young skin, add the forty or so known nutrients from fresh foods eaten as much as possible in their natural state, and mix together with exercise for overall tone and proper breathing for good oxygenation of cells. Put in a dose of fresh air and a pinch of stimulation now and then. Stir well and you've got a recipe that will last for years. That's the theory. In practice, however, things can go wrong: an early wrinkle, acne, dryness, roughness – that's when you need help from special cosmetics, vitamins, and treatments.

When Skin Dries Out

The cause

Dried-out skin usually comes from under-active

sebaceous glands, which don't produce enough of
this important oily fluid to lubricate the skin and
protect it from excessive water loss. It can also be the
result of being exposed to excessively drying weather
conditions, central heating, or air conditioning.
Another, rarer, cause is being on a diet too low in
essential fatty acids, such as a fat-free slimming
regimen. Excessive dryness of the skin also occurs in
people who, unknown to themselves, are suffering
from deficiencies of vitamin A or C or any one of
several of the B-complex group.

Prevention and cure
Use a water-in-oil emulsion on your face night
and day to protect against excessive water loss by
trapping the water in the outer layer of the skin and
preventing it from being given up into the atmos-
phere. Ensure that you get enough essential fatty
acids in your diet by using olive oil in your salad
dressings and cutting out convenience foods full of
junk fats.

Consider taking supplements of vitamins A and
D in the form of fish liver oil, or drinking fresh carrot
juice a couple of times a day and taking some EPA
and DHA in supplement form along with GLA. Try
putting GLA in the form of borage oil or evening
primrose oil directly on the skin too. You need to
leave the oil on the skin for only fifteen minutes;
then you can remove the excess with a tissue.
Vitamin E taken internally and rubbed on the skin
from capsules is often helpful too.

Other helpful things include a humidifier, weekly
steaming of the skin followed by an oil massage, and

mineral water sprayed from an atomizer before applying your moisturizer or treatment products. Don't wash your skin with soap. Don't use any skin product containing alcohol. Use a mask for dry skin. Use aromatherapy oils you mix yourself to contain the essences most useful for dry skin, such as geranium, camomile, rose, sandalwood, lavender, and ylang-ylang. Always choose an oil-based make-up foundation.

Oil Crisis

The cause

Oily skin, or seborrhoea, is the result of overactive sebaceous glands: it usually occurs due to a hormonal imbalance in the body. Occasionally a diet too high in fats and fried foods or refined sugar can contribute to the condition, as can too much stimulation of the sebaceous glands by heat, the sun, or skin-care products. Studies show that people on diets slightly deficient in some of the B group of vitamins rapidly develop whiteheads, blackheads, and oily hair and skin.

Prevention and cure

Treatment for seborrhoea has changed in recent years. Dermatologists used to think the way to deal with the condition was literally to dry out the skin. Dermatologists now realize that oily skin is not the tough and robust stuff they once thought it was. They have found that the use of drying agents in cosmetic products in most cases only treats the problem temporarily by removing excess oil at the expense of worsening the condition in the long run. Attempts to cover it up and to cover up acne with heavy, drying make-up are generally unsuccessful too.

The new approach is different, but it may take time for you to get used to it if you are still thinking in the old way. Instead of using harsh products on your skin, buy a mild, lotion cleanser without any drying agent for cleansing and removing make-up. It should be an oil itself or an oil-in-water emulsion. Rub it on gently with clean hands, then wipe it off completely with tissues before rinsing with fresh, cool water. It is important to remove it all; you don't need a tonic or a freshener, but if you want one, make sure it contains no alcohol (alcohol is also a drier).

During the day, wear a water-in-oil moisturizer and forget the heavy foundation. Instead, as soon as the moisturizer has had a chance to set, powder your face with double the amount of powder you would usually use, dust off the excess, then spray the face with a fine mist of water (preferably spring water from an aerosol, but you can use ordinary water in a spray bottle so long as the spray is very fine). Now blot with a tissue and then powder again. This will keep your skin looking fresh and matt as well as calming the flow of oil from trigger-happy glands. It will also help gradually to shrink the size of your pores. Then, throughout the day, every three or four hours or whenever necessary, you can repowder, and you'll never end up with the ugly, cakey mess oily-skinned women usually get.

Also, stay out of the sun. Sunbathing may dry your skin for a while, but when indoors weather comes you will find you're faced with the results of

the same situation: over-stimulation of the sebaceous glands by ultraviolet light, which results in all
the problems you have been trying to get rid of.

From a nutritional point of view, if your skin is too
oily, don't eat fatty foods or fried foods and do eat
plenty of raw green vegetables and B-complex vitamins from wholegrain breads and cereals, and liver.

The B vitamins (particularly B6, niacin, and B2) in
these foods are vital in the treatment of excessively
oily skin and the acne that often accompanies it.
Vitamin A and beta-carotene can also be useful in
treating skin that is too oily. It can be taken together
with vitamin D as fish liver oil or in higher doses on
its own as well. Vitamin C, potassium, and calcium
have also been reported helpful.

Ultrasensitive and Allergic Skin
The causes
The word allergy means 'altered response' in Greek.
If you are allergic to something, this means that your
body has come into contact with it and instead of
reacting normally to it or not at all, it has reacted
with hostility resulting in raised, red, itchy splotches
on the skin. An acute reaction occurs within seconds
or minutes after coming in contact with the allergen.
You can inhale it, say in the form of a hair spray, or
you can take it in through your skin as a face cream
or a make-up product. There are also delayed reactions, which come about only after a few hours or
even days after coming into contact with the allergen.

Prevention and cure
Apart from nutritional therapy to strengthen the
whole organism against allergic reactions, the only

effective way to deal with skin sensitivities is to be careful about what you put on your face.

Get to know the hypoallergenic cosmetics – skin-care and make-up products made without *known* irritants. Most are inexpensive yet very good and specially formulated with ingredients that have little likelihood of causing problems. The prefix 'hypo' means 'less'. Hypoallergenic products are designed to be less reaction-producing than other cosmetics. They are fragrance-free and leave out such common troublemakers as aluminium salts, wool fat, and phenol.

For immediate relief, skin inflammation usually responds well to calamine lotion, simple witch hazel, and some poultices made with herbs such as calendula. One of the best to use is comfrey, whose very name denotes healing in Latin. It contains the natural anti-inflammatory substance allantoin, which is often used in skin ointments. Make a comfrey compress by pouring half a cup of boiling water over half a cup of the dried herb. Let it cool to a bearable temperature, near body heat, then put the wet herb on the face. Cover with gauze and lie down for fifteen minutes while it cools. This kind of compress will reduce the pain and swelling over a bruise or a pulled muscle, as well as calm inflamed skin.

When Acne Strikes
The cause
Although it is more common among teenagers than among any other age group, acne, an infection of the sebaceous glands, can occur at any time in life. It

shows up as blackheads, whiteheads, pimples, and pustules that occur on the face and neck, back and chest.

The cause of acne is still not completely understood, and the recommended treatment tends to vary. Many people with acne are victims of a food sensitivity or allergy – the most common allergens being wheat, milk, or preservatives and colourings. And when the elimination of waste via the alimentary canal is inadequate, often wastes are eliminated through the skin. Finally, stress and emotional upset are often implicated.

Prevention and cure

Look to your diet first. Eliminate sweets, sugared soft drinks, and fatty foods such as nuts and fried foods. A diet in which at least 50 per cent of your foods are eaten raw often does wonders for even long-term acne, provided it is used in conjunction with the proper external care and vitamin and mineral supplements where necessary.

It is essential to keep the skin clean, removing dirt and excess oil or waxy sebum regularly, using gentle, pH-balanced soaps or detergent cleansers. Skin should be washed in warm water at least twice a day and steamed twice a week to encourage the release of waste matter. Of course your hands should be immaculate so as not to encourage further infection.

Topical agents are often helpful. Retinoic acid, a derivative of vitamin A acid (available only by prescription) applied to the skin is one of the commonly used and generally effective treatments for acne. Sometimes dermatologists use the antibiotic tetracycline, usually administered in doses of 250mg twice a day. In many cases this has dramatically reduced the acne, but there are disadvantages to antibiotic treatment, too. Because of the stress aspects of acne, both regular exercise and meditation or deep relaxation can be helpful too.

Stretch marks

The cause

Stretch marks occur frequently on the abdomen and breasts of pregnant women and on the thighs, hips and buttocks of women who have been over-weight – particularly women who are deficient in zinc, vitamin B6, or both. A sudden increase in weight or volume of an area of the body or the swelling of breasts and abdomen in pregnancy result in these unsightly lines, which are difficult to eliminate.

Prevention and cure

Ensure that you get adequate zinc, silica and vitamin B6 in your diet – if necessary by supplementing it. Women who are on the Pill are particularly sus-ceptible to deficiencies of these two nutrients. If you gain weight or become pregnant, treat your skin from the outside with preventative measures by rubbing on an aromatherapy oil for your skin type twice a day or by the use of cocoa butter.

There is supposed to be no cure for stretch marks once they are formed, for the consistency of the skin itself in that area has changed to resemble scar tissue and therefore remains permanently disfigured. What I have seen is that old stretch marks improve greatly with aromatherapy treatment and connective-tissue massage, which appears to bring life back into the tissue by increasing circulation in the area. But while I have seen them fade greatly – enough for the woman to wear a bikini again without fear of looking ugly – I have never known them to disappear completely.

Blackheads, Whiteheads, and Pimples
The causes
A blackhead consists of a solid plug of oil that clogs the pore and then blackens due to oxidation on exposure to the air. If it is left alone it will simply stay there in the skin. Blackheads do not cure themselves.

A whitehead looks like a tiny white lump on the skin. Once formed, it will remain unless the chemistry of the oil follicle changes, in which case the whitehead turns into a pimple.

Prevention and cure
Blackheads on oily areas of the face (such as around the nose and chin) that are not inflamed can be removed easily by first steaming the skin to open the pores and loosen the oil material. Then gently, with scrupulously clean hands and the tips of your fingers wrapped in facial tissue, you can ease out the plugs. Never use your nails. Finish off the treatment with the application of an antiseptic cream.

If you have many whiteheads it is best to follow nutritional and treatment advice for oily skin. The elimination of a dormant whitehead can only be done by a professional. Besides care in keeping skin clean and nutritional prevention of excessively oily skin, little should be done with a pimple other than to allow it to take its course.

Don't Let Age Get Under Your Skin

Nothing betrays age like the state of your skin. When you are young, it is thick, glowing, soft and elastic. As the years go by, a number of changes take place. To slow down this process and to keep a young healthy skin as long as possible, you have first to retain a young, healthy body. This is a total, ongoing process depending on good nutrition, stress control, exercise, and protection from the environment. There aren't any shortcuts. But the good news is this: these skin ageing changes appear to be not so dependent on the passage of time as they were once believed to be. There is much therefore you can do to retard them.

To Tan or Not To Tan

A tan is a protective reaction. It results from the formation of melanin, the skin's natural pigmentation produced by special cells whose action is triggered by exposure to ultraviolet rays. Every woman has a unique capacity for melanin production, depending on her genetic inheritance. Dark, thick, Mediterranean skins produce more melanin. This is why they will turn a darker brown than the 'English rose' skin, which produces far less. Regardless of the claims they make, there is no tanning product on the market that can promise you a tan of any specific depth.

Sun Worship Without Sun Damage

Sunlight is glorious but watch out. Whether you want to remain wistfully pale or take on a rich, golden colour this summer you need protection. The shorter UVB rays (280–320 mm in length) are strongest in summer and are mostly responsible for burning. UVA rays (320–400 mm) are longer, penetrate much deeper and are responsible for ageing, damage to collagen and the loss of suppleness. Remember that SPF numbers on skin-care products relate solely to UVB rays and how effectively a product filters out the minimal dose of them to cause reddening of the skin. The SPF number indicates the factor by which this minimal dose can be exceeded safely so that if, for instance, you burn after ten minutes in strong sunlight and you apply an SPF 6 you will be protected from burning for up to an hour (6 x 10 minutes). Look for a product that offers good SPF as well as delivering high protection against UVA damage – especially if you have a sensitive skin that is prone to allergies. UVA protection is measured in stars. Four stars is maximum and ideal. Also decide whether you like a cream or lotion. Look for water resistance, then swimming or perspiration won't negate its effectiveness, and use it whenever you are outdoors.

The Tan Accelerators

There are also products on the market that offer not just protection factors but also tanning factors in them. They usually contain a derivative of the essential oil of bergamot, which accelerates the darkening of the skin when it is exposed to ultraviolet rays even in greyish weather. These products can be useful if you want to begin tanning before the strong, midsummer sun appears.

The advantage of tanning this way is that the

melanin which is formed and built up gradually is
your skin's own protection against burning. But it
still won't protect you from ageing. Too much ultraviolet is simply too much. Another disadvantage of
this kind of product is that bergamot is one of the
substances most often responsible for hypersensitive
reactions in women with reaction-prone skin.

Forget the Cigarettes

Smoking also makes skin age rapidly. This is probably because of a substance called benzopyrene,
which is found in cigarette smoke and which uses up
the body's supply of vitamin C rapidly, making it
unavailable for the support of healthy collagen. So
the skin wrinkles earlier.

The skin of smokers wrinkles and ages up to
twenty years sooner than that of non-smokers. But
the problem with cigarette smoke doesn't end there.
For it is not only the smoker whose skin can suffer
from it. So can the non-smoker's. She may take in
considerable quantities of benzopyrene, tar, carbon
monoxide, and other irritating substances just by
being in a room with others who are smoking.

Some dermatologists concerned about the
dangerous effects of cigarette smoke on skin
recommend that every smoker supplement her diet
with additional vitamin C at a rate of 25mg for each
cigarette she smokes. But if you are serious about
preventing ageing, give up smoking altogether – no
matter how difficult it seems and no matter how
many excuses you can make for yourself about why
you think you can't just now.

chapter 2

Hair Help

No woman is ever satisfied with her hair. When it is straight, she wants it curly, and when it is wavy, she wants it straight. The colour is either too light, too dark, or too drab, and she either has too much or too little of it. Fortunately, there are a lot of things you can do for your hair and with your hair to make it more attractive, and more manageable, but it is important to realize from the beginning that you have to work with what you've got. There is no way to change your genetic inheritance, and it is only fruitless and miserable to worry about it.

What Type Are You?

Straight hair is often strong and beautiful hair. It can be lank, in which case you should work it with a 'stripping' shampoo which will enlarge the shaft of each hair and make it look fuller. If it is lacklustre, go for a conditioner to make the scales of the cuticle lie flat and enable hair shafts to reflect light better. Straight hair is often good blunt cut and worn not too long, or tied up in a twist, a braid, or a chignon.

Curly hair needs to be carefully cut, for this can make all the difference between its looking fantastic and frizzy. It is best not to *impose* a particular style on your hair, but, rather, to go with the natural swing of things. If your hair tends to be wiry, you can correct this by using a softening conditioner.

Thin hair must never be allowed to get greasy, for excessive oil on it will only make it look limp and lank. It is usually best to have it cut in a short style, and it is useful to shampoo it often using a shampoo that contains no conditioners, and then use a volumizer – a spray or gel containing polymers which you apply to wet hair before blow-drying. The heat from the dryer swells the polymers that cover the hair shaft, making it look thicker. This will give it bounce and fullness. Blowing it dry helps increase the fullness too.

Fine hair is delicate hair, but it is usually beautiful hair, too, like a baby's. Unlike thin hair, which is caused by a paucity of hair shafts, fine hair is made up of hair shafts of small diameter. You have to be particularly careful about what you do to it, because fine hair is the easiest of all hair types to damage from chemical treatments such as colouring and perming or by using shampoos that are too alkaline, or by exposing it to the sun. Fine hair does well on protein shampoos and needs to be cut superbly and worn short unless you have a great deal of it. Volumizers are useful here, too.

Thick hair is a blessing, although few women who have it realize this – particularly if their hair is curly. In this case, you should probably not wear it too short, or it can be unmanageable. Thick hair is the easiest to handle and the toughest. It will withstand perms and colouring far better than any of the other hair types and may not even need a conditioner at all when it is washed. If it is straight and you decide to get a perm, then you should expect the waving process to take at least a third as long again as it usually does, because the hair shaft is big and tough to break down. But your perm can last you as much as a year, where anyone else's will have to be renewed in a few months.

The Cut is the Thing

A good cut is more important than any other single factor when it comes to the way a head of hair looks. Everyone is an individual, and hairstyling that doesn't take this into account is worse than second-rate. Changing your cut or style every year or two keeps you from getting stuck in a time warp and can lift spirits like nothing else short of falling in love.

Shampooing

There are two types of shampoos: those containing soap and those that are artificial detergents. Modern detergent shampoos do more than just clean. They contain other chemical ingredients, which impart cosmetic properties such as shine and manageability to hair. Certain kinds are particularly good for certain kinds of hair.

Lemon These shampoos are especially good for oily hair, because they help remove the oil without leaving the hair lacklustre and lank.

Balsam This is a good ingredient to choose if your hair is very free or lacks body. Balsam is a resinous substance from the bark of certain trees. In a shampoo, it coats the hair shafts, lending them thickness and strength.

Camomile This is an excellent ingredient for

blonde or light brown hair, since this flower has mild bleaching properties. If you use a camomile shampoo regularly, it helps keep light hair bright and shiny.

Herbs 'Herbs' added to a shampoo doesn't mean a great deal, for many herb formulas (unlike camomile) have no real action on the hair and are created only to appeal to women's back-to-nature feelings. Some, however, such as white nettle, can be useful for dandruff.

Protein Protein shampoos come in two types; both can be useful for hair. The first type contains a simple protein made from eggs, milk, soya, gelatin or beef, which helps to coat the outer layers of the hair, making the hair look thicker. Most protein shampoos are of this type. The second type does far more. Called *substantive protein*, the protein it contains is hydrolysed and of the correct molecular weight and size to be absorbed into the cuticle, strengthening it at the same time as aligning its scales and thickening the shaft. This kind of protein shampoo is particularly good for use on treated, damaged, or free hair.

How often you shampoo depends on you and on the type of hair you have. If it is dry, not more than a couple of times a week is best. If it is normal or oily you can shampoo every day if you like, provided you use a pH-balanced shampoo. However often you do, you need only lather once, unless your hair is really grimy. More than once strips away too much of the hair's natural oils from the cuticle.

Conditioning

Some conditioners contain a large quantity of oil. They are fine for dry hair but will make normal and oily hair into a lank mop that needs to be washed again in the next day or so. Oil-free ones often do a better job in adding body and protecting hair, without causing lankness.

Protein packs or concentrated treatments left on the hair for from five to twenty minutes are excellent as an occasional treatment for hair of all types (say once a month or every six weeks) and exceptionally good for coloured, permed, or damaged hair, used once a week. They will strengthen and protect the hair and leave it soft and shiny. But beware of over-conditioning. It is one of the worst and most commonly unrecognized causes of dull, limp hair. It also shortens the life of any perm significantly.

Styling and Setting

Because the keratin that makes up hair is a protein, like all proteins it can be treated with heat to change its shape. This makes it possible to curl, uncurl, shape, and mould your hair into a particular style by blow-drying it, by setting it wet and allowing it to dry, or by using heated rollers or a curling iron on dry hair.

Blow-drying is an excellent way to style straight or curly hair, provided you have patience and strong arms. If you have dry or brittle hair don't blow-dry it every day as hot air can cause progressive and cumulative damage. If your hair is delicate, choose a dryer that is not too powerful (1,000 watts is enough), as a high wattage may do the job faster but your hair will suffer if you are not extremely careful to keep the dryer far enough from the hair or to use the lowest setting.

Setting your hair can be done wet on rollers or dry on heated rollers, or the hair can be curled dry using a curling iron or a heated brush. A wet set will last you longer, provided you dry it thoroughly under a dryer or in the air. Heated rollers, if you have dry or brittle hair, are something you should not use every day, for they tend to damage the ends of the hair. This can be avoided somewhat by wrapping each roller with a piece of tissue paper or toilet paper before putting it into your hair. Never use heated rollers on wet hair – they won't work. And never use a curling iron on wet hair, or you may damage it badly.

Brushing

Brushing is great for hair, provided you have a good brush and you do not overdo it. It stimulates circulation of the scalp, removes loose scales from the skin on the head, and distributes your hair's natural oils well, which means it helps protect the cuticles and create shine. The brush you choose should have evenly spaced bristles with *rounded* ends. The best brushes for your hair are still made from animal bristles. About 30 to 50 strokes a day is good.

Marvellous Massage

Besides daily brushing, the best thing you can do for the hair is to massage the scalp.

Here's how to massage

Using your fingertips and the palm of your hand just below the thumb, push them firmly into your scalp at the sides and, keeping them in the same place, rotate them in small circles. You will be moving the scalp, not your fingers. It is important that your fingers stay in the same place to stimulate circulation well and so that you never pull your hair. After you have worked in one position for about thirty seconds, remove both hands from your head and take up a new position, rotating your fingertips again firmly for thirty seconds, and so on until you have done your whole scalp. The massage shouldn't take more than three minutes, and it will leave you feeling fresher as well as doing something good for your hair.

Hair Cosmetics

Perms

There are two types of perms: acid-based which are soft and used to give a subtle lift at the roots to create an illusion of fullness; and the conventional alkaline perms. Acid or 'body' perms don't last as long as the rest and need to be redone every three or four months. They are more natural and soft-looking, adding fullness and swing to hair without heavy curls.

Caring for processed hair

Provided your hair is healthy and you look after it well after a perm, there is no reason to worry about its condition being spoiled by the waving. A perm will add a lot of body to lank hair and can often improve an over-oily condition as well.

Once your hair is waved, it is more vulnerable to damage than ever before, so there are a few special precautions you need to take in order to preserve its health and sheen. For instance only use acid-balanced shampoos when you wash your hair, and always apply an acid rinse such as lemon juice in water. Protein treatments are particularly good for permed and coloured hair. Also, instead of brushing 50 strokes a day, cut it down to 20.

If your hair has been bleached or tinted, it is a good idea only to have an acid wave especially designed for bleached or damaged hair. They don't last so long, but they do ensure that the hair remains in good condition.

Straightening hair

Aside from chemical straightening, there are also some short-term but simple ways to straighten hair. It can be done by blow-drying with a brush to smooth it out or by washing your hair and then wrapping it wet around your head in a circle, like a cap, fastening it with clips and letting it dry. Then, when it is dry, you simply comb it out straighter. Finally, the old-fashioned and very efficient method for long, curly hair is simply ironing it with an electric iron. Spread the hair out on a board, keep the iron on the lowest setting, and go over it gently from roots to ends. But the same advice given for blow-drying and heated rollers stands here. Be careful not to put too much heat on it. Burnt hair is irretrievably lost.

A Change of Colour

One of the simplest and most effective ways of changing your appearance is to change the colour of your hair. As we get older, the colour of hair tends to fade so that a once shimmery golden mane or deep mahogany tresses can become lacklustre and dull. Hair colouring these days is effective and reasonably priced and can look even better than most natural hair – provided, of course, it is done correctly.

There are two categories of hair colourants: *permanent* colourants, which cannot be washed out, and the *temporary* and *semipermanent*, which can be used to highlight and intensify your own hair colour.

Temporary colourants

These are the easiest to use. They coat the cuticle of the hair with colour that washes away with the next shampoo. You can get temporary highlighting shampoos and colour rinses in a great variety of colours and most of them have a shine-promoting pH, too. But what you can do with them is limited, for while they will darken the hair – say from blonde to red or to black – they are really designed for minor colour changes only. If you try to go too many shades away from your natural colour, they tend to streak and give uneven coverage and also they cannot make your hair lighter.

Semipermanents

Like the temporaries, they, too, coat the outside of the hair shaft and so are not good for drastically changing hair colour. Nor will they lighten. Some of the semi-permanents are 'colour baths' which penetrate the hair so that they last up to a dozen shampoos. What they are good for is touching up hair that has just started to go grey, highlighting your own natural colouring, and making grey hair look shinier and more attractive without really changing its shade. If you use one, be sure to use a pH-balanced shampoo and a lemon and water rinse afterwards.

The permanents

There are three kinds of permanent hair colourants: vegetable dyes such as henna, metallic dyes such as those used to gradually cover grey hair, and the aniline dyes or oxidation tints, which include most of the colourants used professionally in salons.

The vegetable dyes

Henna will give brunette and black hair a lovely reddish glow; the darker your hair the more chestnut is the effect. Lighter hair goes Titian. Henna does not do well on mousy hair, as the resulting tone is usually an unattractive orange. It should never be used over a tint, is no good on grey hair, and can be very drying to any hair, so it is better to avoid it if your hair is already dry. The only colour of henna you should use is red, which in its natural, powder form, is a pale green.

The standard way of using henna is to add hot water to make a creamy paste and then put this on the hair and leave it for up to one hour. Daniel Galvin, Britain's top colourist, who is an expert in the use of herbal hair colourings, uses a different method and gets beautiful results. He adds hot black coffee to the powder, mixes it into a paste, and then adds the juice of a fresh lemon and the yolk of an egg. The coffee brings out the depth and richness of the hair colour, the acid in the lemon accelerates the reddening, and the egg yolk keeps the mixture moist and easy to manoeuvre through the hair. Sometimes he also adds some 10 per cent peroxide to lighten the whole effect.

Camomile, another herbal colourant, has a gentle lightening effect on hair and is wonderful for 'sun-streaking' blonde and light brown hair. But you must be patient, for it takes several applications and plenty of time to work. It is not useful for brown hair or dark hair, but it will gently lighten red and works beautifully on all shades of natural blonde. The herb also adds shine to the hair.

You can make a camomile rinse to use after each shampoo (as the last rinse) by taking 2 tablespoons of dried camomile flowers and tossing them into a pint of boiling water. Simmer for fifteen minutes, strain, cool and use as a final rinse (you can make more at once and refrigerate it for up to ten days). You leave the rinse in your hair and towel it dry.

Metallic dyes

These are often called *colour restorers*. They deposit metallic dyes and salts of various metals such as manganese, cobalt, silver, and copper on your hair shaft, which gradually darken the hair. But hair dyed this way does not perm well, nor is its condition very good, as this kind of dye tends to make the hair look a dull, flat colour. Metallic dyes have to be removed completely, with the use of a special preparation, several days before waving or tinting with a permanent colourant. Because of their many disadvantages, I think they are best avoided.

Aniline or oxidation colourants

The most permanent (and the most successful), these dyes are included in a number of products for colouring hair such as tinting shampoos, highlighting shampoos, and the single-step and double-step permanent colourants you can buy in packages at the chemist. It is important whenever using a permanent colourant on your hair either at home or at the hairdresser, that a patch test be done first. The anilines can even cause blindness, so they should never be used to tint eyelashes or eyebrows. If you have your hair dyed with an aniline dye, you must wait at least a week before having it permanent-waved or straightened, and you must use a pH-balanced shampoo and conditioner every time you wash it.

One of the advantages of the anilines is that tinting limp, straight hair that won't hold a set can often make it more manageable.

The single and double-step tints also fall into this category. They are the dyes most frequently used by hairdressers. If you want to change the colour of your hair dramatically, you should have it done professionally. There is quite an art to colour mixing and application (I know women who fly 5,000 miles to have their colour done by someone who is a real master at it).

Special Care for Coloured Hair

The golden rule for processed hair is to stay out of the sun. The sun does harm in two ways: it dries out the hair, and it alters the colour.

If you are going into the sun and your hair is bleached or tinted, wear a hat or a towel wrapped around it. Even virgin – that is, untreated – hair needs protection from sunlight. You can use one of the sunscreen products especially made for hair or simply rub in some high-protection suntan lotion you use on your body, shampooing it out at the end of the day.

Hair Loss

Each day, you can expect to lose between 100 and 200 hairs. So you shouldn't be discouraged when you look down at the pillow in the morning to see a few lying there. This only means that new hairs will quickly be growing. That is, provided your hair is not coming out by the handful. Sometimes, as a result of sudden shock, hormonal change, or illness, large numbers of hairs are lost all at once. Even this is nothing to worry about unduly, so long as whatever triggered the loss is either past (as in the case of childbirth) or being corrected with a relaxation technique and dietary supplements for undue stress or illness.

chapter 3

The Eyes Have It

Not only are your eyes the truest of all physical reflections of who you are, they are also an ageless expression of beauty. For there can be something breathtaking about the eyes of an old woman, as there is about the eyes of a child. Like any other part of your body, to be beautiful your eyes have to be healthy, and to be healthy they need care.

But the care they need is quite different from what we are usually led to believe. For eyes are *not* the delicate, poor, vulnerable things we have been taught they are – overworked, constantly struggling against inadequate light and overstrain, and longing for some well-deserved tinted glasses to rest them. Far from it. Your eyes are tough. They were made for use, all kinds of use, and the more you use them, to read and to see with – both far away and up close – and the more you exercise the muscles around them, and the more they are exposed to the full spectrum of natural sunlight, the healthier and more beautiful they can become. And not only will your eyes benefit, so will the rest of your body.

Cool Shades

For the sake of your health and vitality, it is important to spend at least an hour a day out in the open with your eyes exposed to the sunlight – not guarded behind lenses, whether the lenses be glasses or window panes or car windscreen. Wear sunglasses when you need them, by all means, but don't wear them incessantly as a fashion accessory. Your eyes and the rest of your body *need* light.

When buying a pair of sunglasses, be sure to test them for optic clarity and quality. Hold them at arm's length, and looking through one lens at a slender vertical image, such as the frame of a door, watch to see if it remains still while you wiggle them up and down. If it does, they are properly made. If not, try a different pair. Look for sunglasses that state what percentage of the ultraviolet spectrum they absorb. For wearing in bright sunlight, they need to be dark enough to eliminate 70-85 per cent. Also check that the lenses have a scratch-resistant surface.

Eye Care

How, physically, you handle your eyes has a lot to do with how long the skin around them looks young and how clear and bright they are themselves. Eyes don't need to be favoured to stay beautiful and healthy, but they don't need abuse, either. Yet they are faced with it most of the time, in the form of air pollution, smoke, misapplied make-up, and mismanaged make-up removal.

The skin surrounding your eyes is thinner and finer than anywhere else on your face. It is also only sparsely supplied with oil glands and therefore highly prone to expression lines. This is where a good eye cream can help. They come in several varieties. Some (usually the more expensive) are designed not only to protect the skin in the area from dehydration but also to plump it up for several hours to minimize the lines there. They are particularly good for women over forty with dry skin, but the plumping action is highly transient. You have to keep using them once you start or your eyes quickly revert to the way they looked before.

Others, particularly the herbal gels, are soothing and cooling. Very slightly astringent, this sort of eye cream will help calm swollen lids. If you don't want to spend money on eye cream, a rich oil such as avocado, hazelnut, or apricot dabbed on, in the *barest* traces, around the eye area will do just as good a job, used mornings before applying make-up and evenings before bed – provided you are not after the tightening effect.

When you put on your oil or eye cream matters. It is important never to use too much of it or you can end up with swollen, irritated eyes, particularly if you are using the plumping-up variety. Apply it gently with your third finger (there is less pressure that way) tapping lightly all around the eye. Never rub or pull the skin.

How you apply mascara and how you remove it matters too. Most women open their eyes wide and look directly into the mirror, wrinkling up their forehead in the process. The best way is to hold your mirror at chin level and look down into it; then you don't etch wrinkles into your forehead. This may not seem very important, but when you think that you apply mascara, say twice a day, probably every day of your adult life, the habitual creasing of the forehead becomes a significant force in creating wrinkles there. You will get better coverage, too.

Think twice before you opt for waterproof mascara. It is difficult to remove, so you need a special strong remover to do it and you can end up rubbing and irritating the eye area every time you take off your make-up. Unless you go walking in the rain or swimming with your make-up on, it is better to choose a conventional variety. To take it off, use a non-oily eye-make-up remover if your eyes are sensitive (most are), and saturate a pad of absorbent cotton with it. Then put the pad over the closed eye and hold it there for ten seconds to dissolve the make-up so you can easily stroke it away.

Tips and Tricks

Here are some useful treatments for such common troubles as red and irritated eyes, black circles, and puffy lids:

Tired eyes

Close your eyes tightly, then more tightly, pressing the lids together as hard as you can. Now open them slowly. This is good for when you are stuck in traffic and your eyes are tired from driving, or if you have been reading for a long while, or when you wake up and find your vision is not clear.

Put your elbows on the table in front of you and close your eyes. Then cover them with the palms of your hands. Press gently against the whole eye area for a minute or so. This refreshes the eyes and, provided you breathe deeply and calmly while you are doing it, also revitalizes the rest of you.

Swollen eyes

Do the palming exercise (above) and then cover your eyes with cold compresses made from absorbent cotton dipped in ice-cold eyebright tea (1 tablespoon of the dried herb to a cup of water). Or lie down for ten minutes with grated raw potatoes between two pieces of gauze on your lids.

Red and irritated eyes

Dip your hands into ice-cold water and then press them against your eyelids, dipping and pressing several times. Put a slice of cucumber on each closed lid while resting for five minutes.

Black circles

Are you anaemic? Retaining wastes? Are your kidneys not working optimally? Do you have a low-grade infection? All of these things can cause dark-rimmed eyes. But one of the most common causes is poor elimination or the retention of toxic wastes in the system. A vitamin B12 deficiency should also be suspected.

chapter 4

Face Magic

When you use make-up, you are practising the age-old art of illusion for enhancement. But the illusions make-up offers you are subtle ones, not complete changes of character, age, and colouring. The first rule of good make-up is simple: never try to *change* your face with it.

Having said that there is a lot you can do with colour to make you feel better. And that, after all, is what making up your face is all about. The make-up you choose and the way you apply it should make you look more attractive, more interesting, healthier, and simply more yourself.

The Tools

The brushes you use, the sponges and cotton-wool, and even your mirror and lighting are all important in getting good results from your make-up products. You need to acquire a collection of them, keeping your tools immaculately clean and using them *every* time you put on your make-up.

Here is a suggested list of makeup tools as a general guideline.

Make-up tools

2 large brushes	for powder
3 slightly smaller brushes	for blusher, highlighter, and shader
1 blunt-ended brush	for blending concealers
4 small brushes	for eye shadows and for highlighting small areas
1 stiff toothbrush-like or circular brush	for brows
1 circular hard tiny brush	for clearing excess mascara from lashes (this can be saved from a used mascara wand and then washed thoroughly)
1 fine-line lip brush Cotton-wool balls or pads and cotton-tipped sticks	for clearing away mascara accidentally smeared on your face and lipstick that has gone where it shouldn't have.
Facial tissues A spray bottle	used for misting plants, filled with pure spring water. The spray should be very fine to cover your skin with a delicate mist, not drops of water.
Good light	either natural light (which is best for applying any kind of make-up, because it gives a true picture of what colours are doing on your face) or ordinary incandescent lighting, which is second best. Get as much light as possible – certainly on both sides of the mirror you are using. Fluorescent lighting is bad for make-up: it grossly distorts colours.
A scarf	to tie back your hair.

In addition, you will want some *sponges* for applying foundation and liquid blushers. They can be either natural sponges (the tiny ones used for cosmetics) or white rubber sponges. I think the natural ones are best.

It is important to keep your tools and brushes for make-up immaculate. The brushes can be washed in warm water with a little detergent shampoo or simple soap and then left to dry naturally in the air. Wash your make-up sponges at least once a week in soap or shampoo and keep them well aired and ready for use.

The Products

Make-up products offer you several things: coverage, which to some extent will conceal minor flaws and blemishes in your skin, luminescence, and most important, colour. There are literally hundreds of different makeup products on the market. From the amount of advertising that accompanies the launch of each of them you would assume that a woman needs all of them. You don't; in fact you need very few.

The Colours

The idea that make-up colour – say an eye shadow – is only to be used on the eyes, or a blusher only on cheeks, is absurd. Colour is colour, and it doesn't matter what you call a product, provided it serves the purposes you want it to. The colours that you use on your face should all give *support* to each other so they work together to create an overall effect that is pleasing.

There are two basic possibilities: warm colour schemes and cool ones. The effect of a warm colour scheme on the face, which includes the earth colours such as browns, greens, beiges, golds, yellows, apricots, coppers, oranges, and peaches, is to enliven it, making your face look healthier and stronger and more glowing. Warm colours look wonderful on older women, too, because they accentuate youth. This is why some of the best foundations and powders now contain yellow pigments. A little peach or apricot blusher can make almost any face look younger, whereas bluish-pink blusher applied to a face over forty can age it drastically.

The cool colours – the blues, purples, pale ivories, silvers, fuchsias, berries, magenta, blue-pinks, and whites – give a look of delicate vulnerability to a face, especially when they are applied, as they should be, over a very pale foundation. But to wear them you have to have perfect skin and you have to be young; otherwise they can make you look tired, older, and even unwell.

Practice Makes Perfect

The only way to learn about using make-up is by experimenting with it over and over again until using it well becomes second nature. Set aside some time to yourself – about forty-five minutes a month, say, in which you simply sit in front of your mirror and experiment with make-up colours and textures, to see the kind of effects you can get.

The Moisturizer

Every good make-up begins with a fine moisturizer complete with sunscreen lavishly applied over clean skin and then given a chance to settle in. You need to wait for your skin to take to the moisturizer before you put on your foundation, otherwise you will end up with a flawed finish and your make-up will not last. 'Taking' time is usually between two to five minutes.

In addition to the ordinary moisturizers, there are also tinted ones on the market. These products are halfway between moisturizers and foundations. They impart some colour and also provide you with some measure of protection from water loss. They give a very light cover but can be a nice way of simply adding a healthy glow to your skin. Some of them also contain sunscreens. When choosing a tinted moisturizer, look for one that is not too far away from your own skin tone, or you will find it doesn't blend in and cover well.

Among the tinted moisturizers are the 'colour correctives' – products tinted a specific hue in order to change the look of your own, natural colouring. They are worn under your ordinary foundation. A green moisturizer will soften a florid skin, toning it down and making it look more neutral. Green will also help conceal red blotches and spots on your skin. A mauve-coloured moisturizer can improve a dull complexion and brighten the face of someone who is too pale. An apricot-coloured corrective should be used only by the very few women who are really sallow. When you use a corrective, put it on with a sponge that has been dampened and then had all the excess water removed from it by wiping it against a towel.

The Foundation

Once your moisturizer has set, you are ready for the foundation. But why all over? Instead you can wear it only on parts of your face such as around the eyes, where it gives a good base for eye shadows, on your chin, and on your cheeks. The advantage to this is that you still get the wonderful, delicate shading of natural skin, rather than that all-over deadness that can come from covering your whole face with one opaque colour. Or you can wear two shades of foundation: a lighter one in the centre of your face (on the nose, forehead, cheeks, and chin) and the slightly darker one of the same tone around the out-side (near the hairline and along the jawline). This has the effect of preserving a natural-looking grada-tion of colour and still lending the finished look of a well-made-up face.

A foundation is not *meant* to give strong colour to a face. It is supposed to be flat and neutral. About 80 per cent of Caucasian skin should wear one foundation colour: a flat, true beige with neither pink nor peach overtones to it. It will look good on all ages of 'northern European' skin, because it gives a neutral canvas on which to put your eye and lip colours.

If your skin is olive or yellowish or very dark, then choose a foundation as close to its natural colour as possible but slightly flatter. When testing out colour, put it on your naked face, and then again go out into the daylight to look at the results before buying any-thing. The kind of foundation you choose depends on what kind of skin you have as well as on personal preference. Dry skin does best with a cream or oil-based liquid foundation. Ageing skin needs the finest of liquid foundation. Anything heavily oily collects in the lines and makes you look haggard. Oily skin demands a water-based liquid or cream or a cake or block-type make-up. Put a little foundation in the palm of your hand and then dip the sponge into it and apply it to your face, brushing it lightly over your skin again and again until everything is well blended into your skin.

The Concealer

Now is the time to deal with any problems you want to conceal, such as black circles under your eyes or discolourations here and there. Concealer creams and sticks are good here, although some of them are greasy and, particularly under the eyes, tend to sink into tiny lines and make matters worse. Put your concealer on with a flat wedge-shaped brush and smooth into the skin until it blends perfectly with the surrounding areas. If you add a little powder here you will get just the finish you need to make the undesirable area fade into the surrounding skin tones.

Secrets of Light and Shade

The secret of making light and shade work for you is simply to apply both sparingly and only where it matters to your face, and always to blend well into the surrounding area. Whatever part of your face you want to bring out or emphasize, you apply a light colour to, and whatever part you want to minimize, you cover with a darker shade.

Here are some of the things you can do with shading:

● *To minimize a jaw that is too large or too square*, apply darker shade along the jawline, blending it under the jaw and fading into nothing at the sides of the face.

- *To shorten a pointed chin*, apply shader to chin only, blending underneath into the neck and fading to nothing at the sides.

- *To fade a double chin*, put shader on the double chin and blend it skilfully. This will make it recede into the background and look less prominent.

- *To give more interesting shape to a square face*, apply shader in the temple area and all around the jaw-line, carefully blending.

- *To minimize a nose that is too large*, apply shader in a single stripe down the centre of the nose, carefully blending into the colour at the sides so that no definite line appears.

- *To slim a broad nose*, apply a shader – preferably a slightly darker foundation or cream – in a stripe down each side of the nose and blend it carefully into the skin to make the nose look narrower.

The Eyes Have It

For most women, one of their best features is the eyes. Perhaps this is because eyes reveal so much of what goes on inside one. Make-up for eyes should emphasize this and show off the eyes' beauty and colour.

There are lots of ways to use eye make-up to improve eyes, but all of them begin with the same principles. Use neutral tones such as slabby browns (without red tones in them), flat greys, and greyed greens, or even terracotta, for establishing the shape of the eyes (the darker shades to define the sockets and the lighter beiges or yellow, peach or apricot, or pink, on the lids and under the brows).

All eye shadows are best applied to skin that has a foundation on it even if you don't put foundation on the rest of your face, and powder shadows hold best over a light skimming of translucent powder too. All eye shadows are best applied with a brush, whether they are liquid, cream, or powder. You will get a better, longer-lasting finish from them this way.

Eyebrow Sculpture

Before you begin, brush your eyebrows first one way and then the other to remove any loose hairs or make-up, and clean the skin around the eyes thoroughly. Now put moisturizer in the area, before you reach for the tweezers. Brush your brows into shape and take a good look at them. Start by removing stray hairs between the brows and the stragglers but never pluck from above the eyebrow. And always remove only one hair at a time, pulling it in the direction in which it grows. When you have finished with one brow, apply antiseptic or a simple toner to it before going on to the next one. This will help soothe the irritated skin. Don't try to apply make-up for an hour after plucking ends.

The Eyelids

Apply the lighter shade of coloured shadow you have chosen to the section of the lid nearest the lashes, and then brush it out, fading it away to nothing towards the eyebrows. Now you can have the darker shadow in the socket to define the shape. Remember that colours on the outer edges of your eyes will tend to widen the look of your face and open your gaze.

Finally put on your eyeliner. A good way of emphasizing eye shape without looking too obviously made-up is to use a pencil in the same tone you are using for your eye shadow, dotting it all along the upper lashes and then just under the lower ones so the two lines meet at the outer corners and form a little triangle. This kind of liner looks good when it is gently smeared with a brush or fingertip to blend it into the surrounding area and keep it from looking hard. You can also use another colour line drawn on the *inside* of the lower lid if you like.

The other way of applying eyeliner is with a brush, in which case you use liquid or cake liner and get a more definite line. It is drawn just above the roots of the upper lashes and just below the roots of the lower ones, again meeting at the corner. Many women use black eyeliner, but usually a gentle grey or slate or muted brown is better.

The Mascara

Mascara makes eyes look more glamorous. It seems to create an aura of mystery about the eyes when lashes are darkened and thickened. Unless you are planning to walk in the rain or to go swimming with your make-up on, you are better off using a mascara that is not waterproof.

The Cheeks

Here, the best colours for everyday wear for most women are terracotta, apricot-brown or dusky peach, because they make the skin look particularly healthy. Used high on the cheekbones they accentuate a well-sculptured face. Used across the cheeks they give a simple warm glow.

The Lips

Most women tend to pick lipsticks that are too bright or too pink to flatter their colouring. There is certainly a place for fire-engine reds and vivid fuchsias, but for everyday wear you are probably better off with a muted brownish pink or a softened melon or salmon. Shop around until you find four or five lipsticks in differing tones that look good on you.

When applying lipstick, use a pencil or a lip brush to outline your mouth first, so you get a good, sharply defined edge. Then apply your lipstick and blot it and apply again if you want it to stay. Alternatively use a pencil all over the mouth as well as for outline and then apply a clear gloss. It looks fresh and simple and the colour tends to last. Frosted lipsticks are for the very young. Older women are usually better off with cream lipsticks, since frosting shows up wrinkles on the lips and the see-through ones don't give enough definition.

The Powder

A little translucent powder that imparts no colour but gives a smooth, matt finish can actually make a face look younger. It is also an interesting effect to powder only parts of your face, such as the sides below the cheekbones, the nose, and the forehead, and then leave a sheen on cheeks and chin. Always use a powder that gives no colour, just a matt, smooth finish, and always brush away every speck of excess once you have applied it.

The Finishing Touches

Last of all, after you have applied your make-up completely, you need to set it with water. This step is very useful, for it will make a face last far longer than it otherwise would. Spray your face with spring water from an aerosol can or with a fine mist from a plant-misting bottle. Then blot gently once with a tissue.

The whole process of making up may sound complicated, but with practice it should take very little time – no more than ten minutes from start to finish.

Nails to Flaunt

Beautiful nails are no accident. A few fortunate women seem to have been born with genes which lend themselves to the growth of long, strong nails but the rest of us have to work at it. The encouraging thing is that a little work – some changes in nutrition plus a new regime of external care – can transform your nails within a few months.

Why weak nails?

The standard advice (still, sadly, given by a lot of so-called nail experts) is that if your nails are weak or thin or break easily, you need to eat lots of protein to correct the condition. It is this assumption that leads manicurists to suggest gelatin capsules for weak nails. But it is a false one. Very soft nails most often announce not a protein deficiency, but either a mineral deficiency or hypochlorhydrin: lack of sufficient stomach acid. This prevents the adequate production of amino acids from which nails can be built.

One of the best possible overall treatments for nails is to go on a six-week course of nutritional supplementation aimed at eliminating hypochlorhydrin. This means taking three 500 mg capsules of a good blend of amino acids (ideally formulated to mimic the balance found naturally in an egg), together with one or two tablets of betaine hydrochloride and three to six kelp tablets after each meal. It is a method which tends to work even when all others fail. For anyone who has consistently struggled with the problem of poor nails it can be a real blessing.

Nail saver tips

Without becoming obsessive, there are certain precautions you can take to help protect your nails from physical damage:

- Use a pencil to dial the telephone.

- Use a knuckle rather than your fingertip to push buttons, for example to call a lift.

- Keep hand lotion ready to use after you wash your hands and during the day.

- Use rubber gloves every time you wash the dishes.

The French Manicure

Part of the fun of looking glamorous is having ten beautiful lady-of-leisure nails to waft about. Yet who wants to spend their life wearing protective gloves and worrying about the 'catastrophe' of breaking a nail? Learn the French manicure secrets for strong nails and then you can renew your manicure just once a week.

You need: nail varnish remover, cotton wood pads, emery board or nail soak, orange stick, cuticle trimmer, nail scissors, buffer (optional), base coat, nail varnish, top coat.

The pre-manicure

If you are short on time, just do steps 1 and 2. Save the longer pre-manicure for really pampering yourself.

1. Filing

It is best to file your nails while they still have polish on so that they are afforded some protection. Keep the sides of the nails straight and only file the corners in a gentle curve. Follow the natural shape of your nails as a guide and file away from the outer edge towards the centre in one direction.

2. Cleaning

Soak a cotton pad with a remover containing conditioner and press it onto the nail for a few seconds, then wipe it outwards away from the cuticle. If you have been wearing coloured varnish you may need to soak a cotton bud with remover and go around the edge of the cuticle to help lift away any remaining colour. If your nails are stained , use a cut piece of lemon to help dissolve the stain and whiten them.

3. Soaking

Soak your fingertips in a bowl of warm water containing a conditioning nail soak. You can make your own using a few drops of your favourite bath oil dissolved in water.

4. Cuticle care
Rinse your hands and pat them dry. Using an orange stick, gently push back your cuticles. This will make your nails appear longer.

5. Top abrasion
This step can be helpful if your nails have bad ridges while you are waiting for the nutritional supplements to affect the new nail growth. Also, if you do not like to wear nail varnish, you can get a polished look naturally. Using a special flexible buffing board with three different grades of roughness on it, simply buff the nail in one direction several times. Start with the heaviest grade and work towards the finest.

6. Final squeak
Rub over each nail once more with a cotton pad soaked in nail varnish remover to prepare an oil-free base on which to apply your varnish.

The manicure
Three steps to success:

1. The base
Apply a layer of protective base coat to each nail. Look for a base coat which incorporates nail strengthener.

2. Tip treat
Paint the tip of each nail – the white part – with white enamel. This can be matt white or pearlized white. Not only does this keep your nails looking fresh and clean but, more importantly, it gives them extra strength at the tips where they need it. Let the tips dry and then add another tip coat.

3. Top

Finish the manicure by applying a layer of top coat to the entire nail to seal the lacquers. To keep your manicure fresh and protect your nails even further, paint a coat of top coat over the top of your manicure every evening and massage a little cuticle cream into your cuticles.

Finally

I have always found the Biblical expression 'Become what thou art' full of meaning. Becoming beautiful is like that. But it is not a static state of perfection, as the glossy magazines would have us believe – one fleeting moment on a well-made-up, well-lit face, captured for eternity by the camera. It is a living process, an unfolding of your uniqueness no matter what your age or where you start from – a kind of journey which, for me, is one of the two most exciting things in life. The other, I believe, is creativity itself, whether it is expressed in painting a picture, cooking a meal, running a business, loving a man or caring for a child. And the wonderful thing about the whole process of becoming what you really are is that it inevitably leads to greater creativity and satisfaction in what you do. What could be better than that?

Further Reading

If you found this book useful you might like to read other titles by Leslie Kenton. All are available from good bookshops or simply telephone Murlyn Services on 01279 427203. Titles include:

The Dynamic Health Series: a short series of collectibles on every subject – quick to read, practical and life-changing.

● **10 Day Clean-up Plan** (Ebury Press, £6.99)
A step-by-step guide to regenerating your energy while transforming the way you look and feel – all in ten days.

● **Raw Energy Recipes** (Ebury Press, £6.99)
Eating lots of fresh, raw foods can help you look and feel younger, and protect against colds, flu, fatigue and stress.

● **Cellulite Revolution** (Ebury Press, £6.99)
This plan revolutionizes, rebalances and re-establishes a healthy body ecology so you can live cellulite-free forever.

● **10 Day De-Stress Plan** (Ebury Press, £6.99)
Learn how to master stress with a minimum of fuss and a maximum of pleasure. Start now to make stress a friend forever.

● **Lean Revolution** (Ebury Press, £6.99)
Calorie controlled diets don't work. This book shows you how to eat more to shed fat the energy way.

● **Raw Energy Food Combining Diet** (Ebury Press, £6.99)
Food combining is a smart way to shed unwanted fat without counting a calorie and it will make you feel more alive.

● **Juice High** (Ebury Press, £6.99)
Discover how raw fruit and vegetable juices can energise your life, rejuvenate your body, expand your mind & free your spirit.

The Classic Series: each book a bible combining up-to-date scientific research with the time-tested principles of natural health and beauty.

● **The New Joy of Beauty** (Vermilion, £9.99)
Real beauty is nothing less than the full expression of the individual nature of a woman. *The* bible to health and beauty.

● **The New Ageless Ageing** (Vermilion, £8.99)
A marriage of high-tech science and natural health, this book offers a complete anti-ageing programme.

● **The New Ultrahealth** (Vermilion, £8.99)
The latest research into high-energy health allows you to explore the heights of well-being, physically and emotionally.

● **The New Biogenic Diet** (Vermilion, £8.99)
Health, nutrition and permanent weight loss based on natural fresh foods which have been carefully combined.

● **The New Raw Energy** (Vermilion, £8.99)
This meticulously researched work shows how fresh, un-cooked foods can work wonders for your body and your life.

Also by Leslie Kenton:

Passage to Power (Vermilion, £9.99)
Few women in our culture are prepared for menopause, nor for the next phase of their life. Exploring the biochemistry and physiology of menopause, alongside myth and archetype, this book will transform the lives of women over 35.

Nature's Child (Ebury Press, £6.99)
How to raise a happy, healthy, independent child the natural way.

Endless Energy (Vermilion, £9.99)
Using simple yet potent energy-enhancing techniques for your body, mind and spirit, learn how to realise your full potential and reach new heights of good looks, creativity and joy.

Index